Gourmet Cooking for Everyone